Jon Scieszka's Trucktown

Oh No!

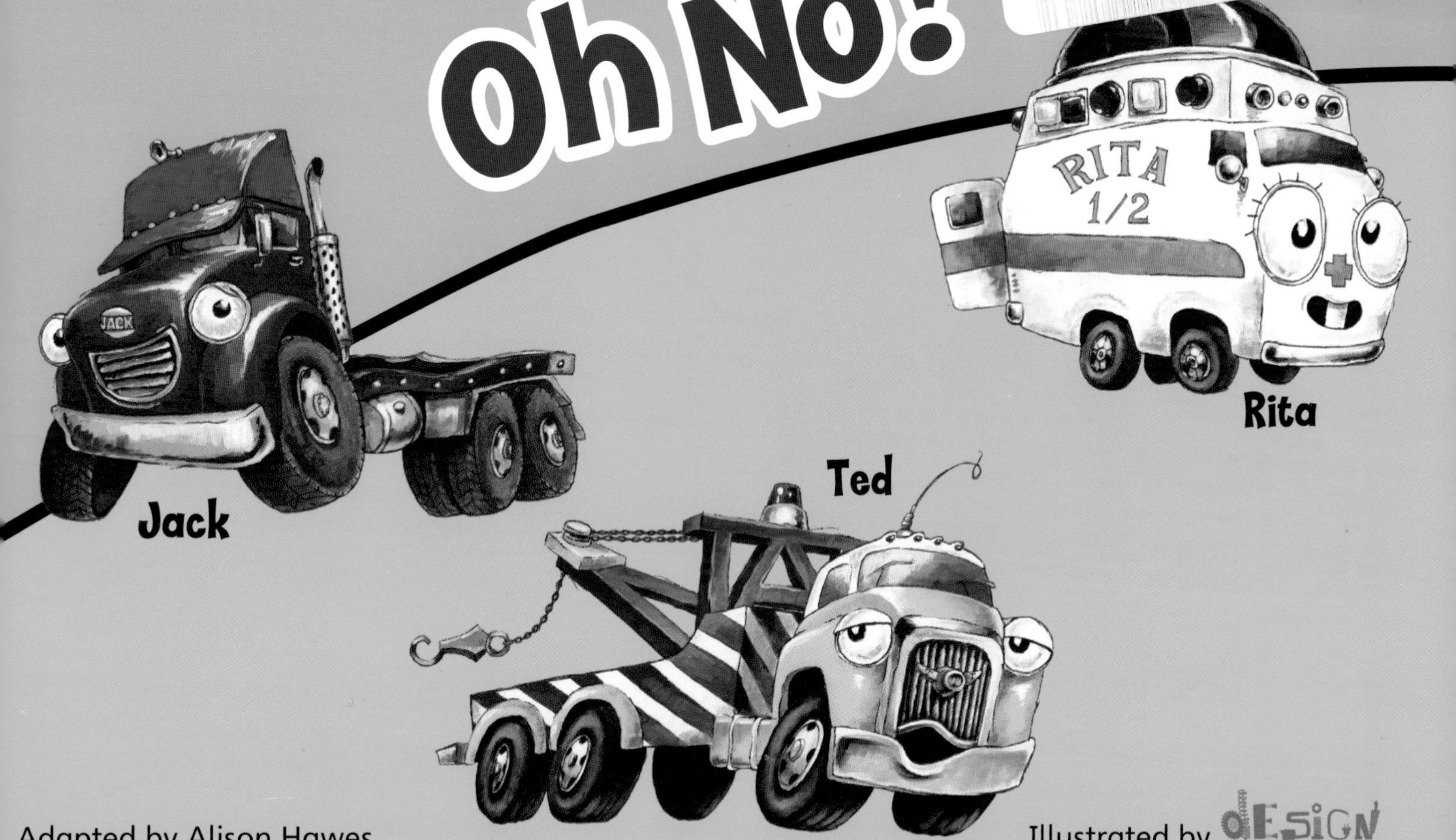

Adapted by Alison Hawes

Illustrated by Design Garage

Snow

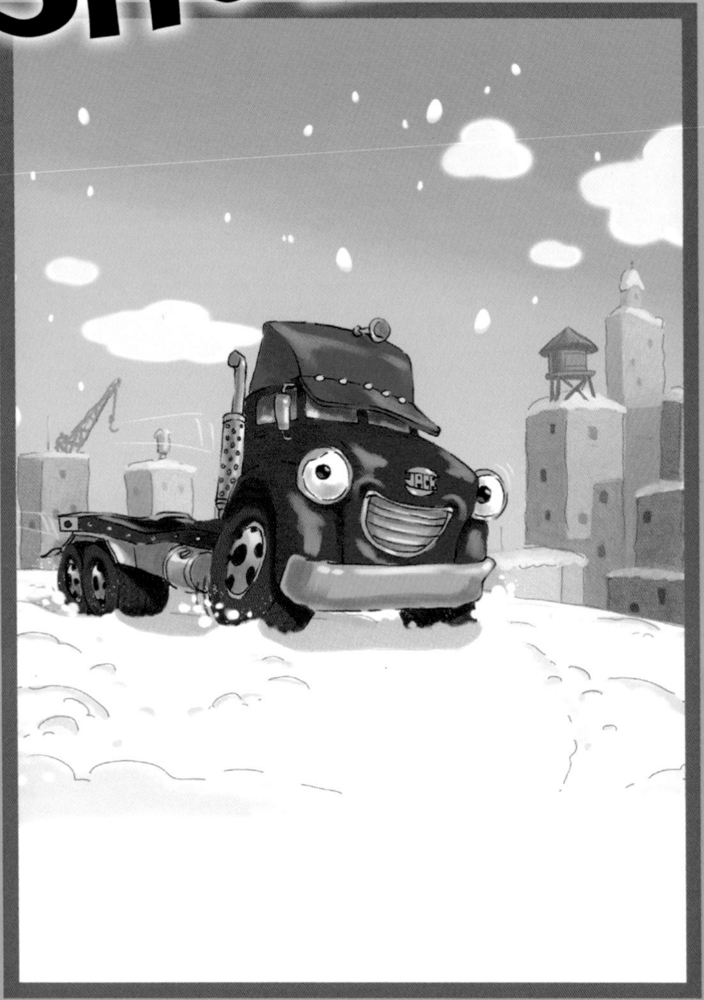

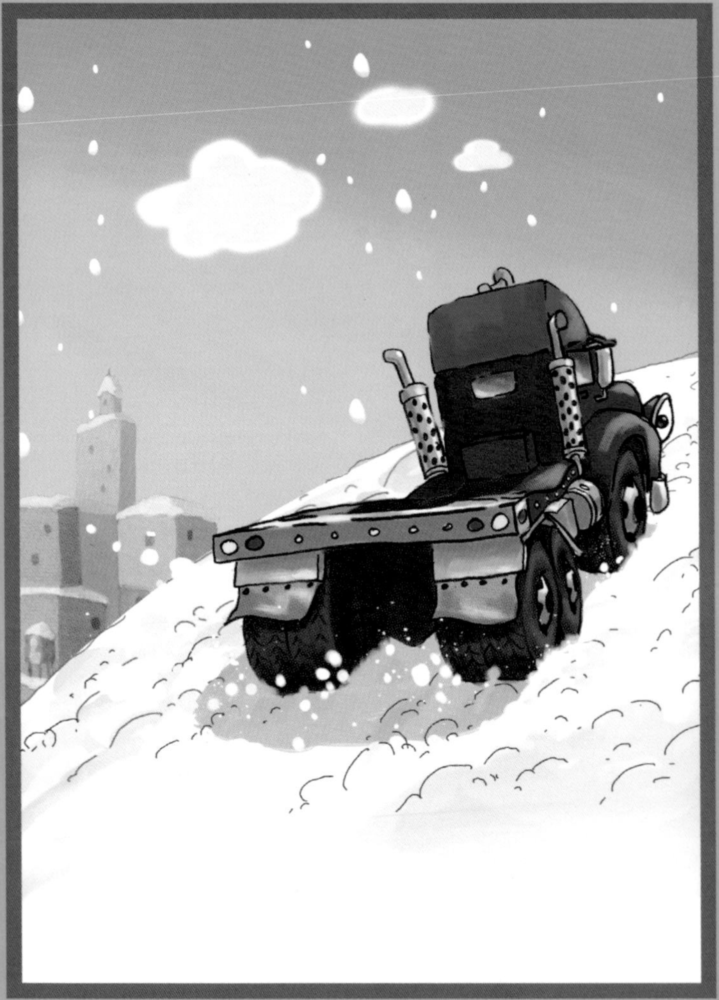

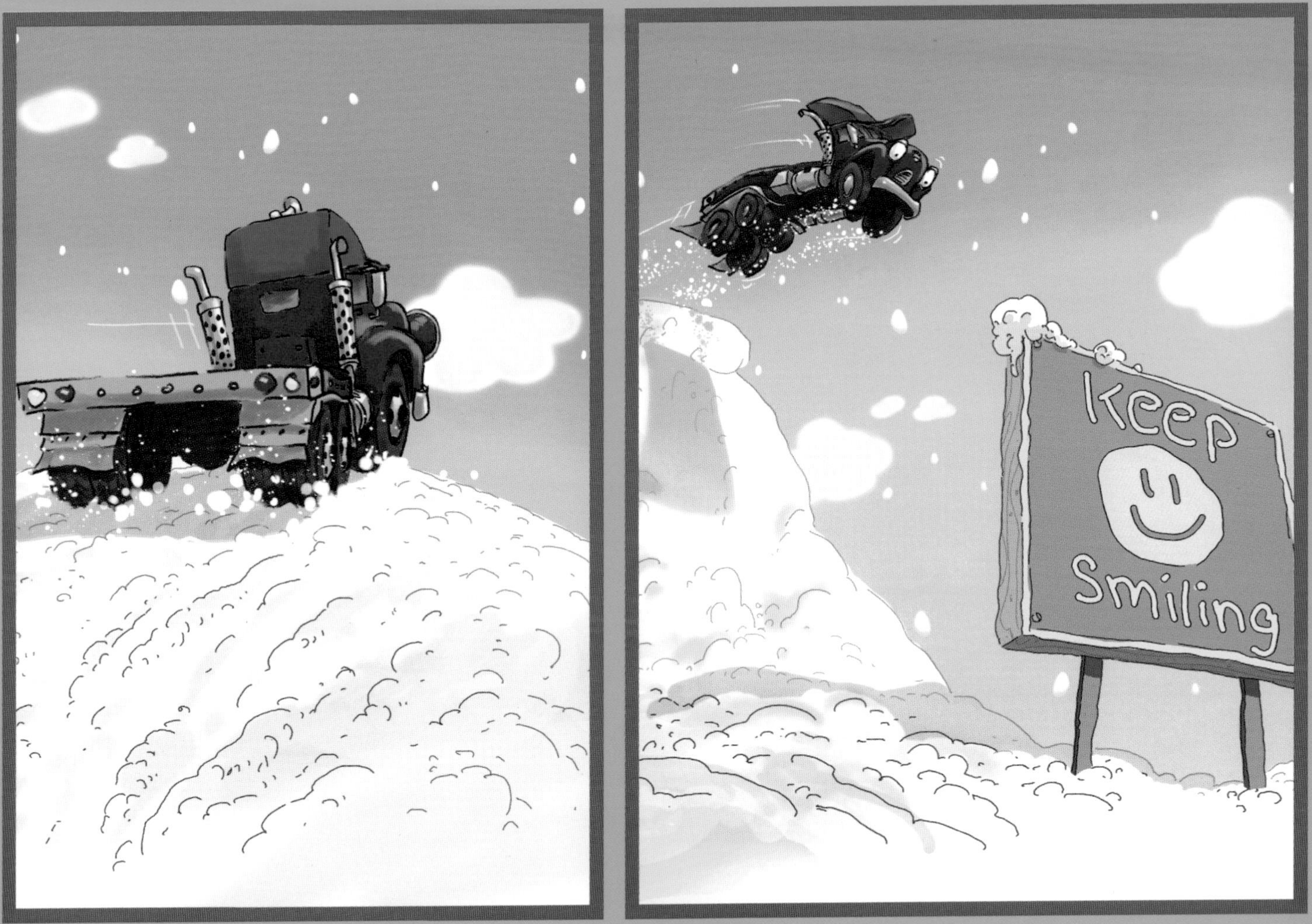
Keep
Smiling

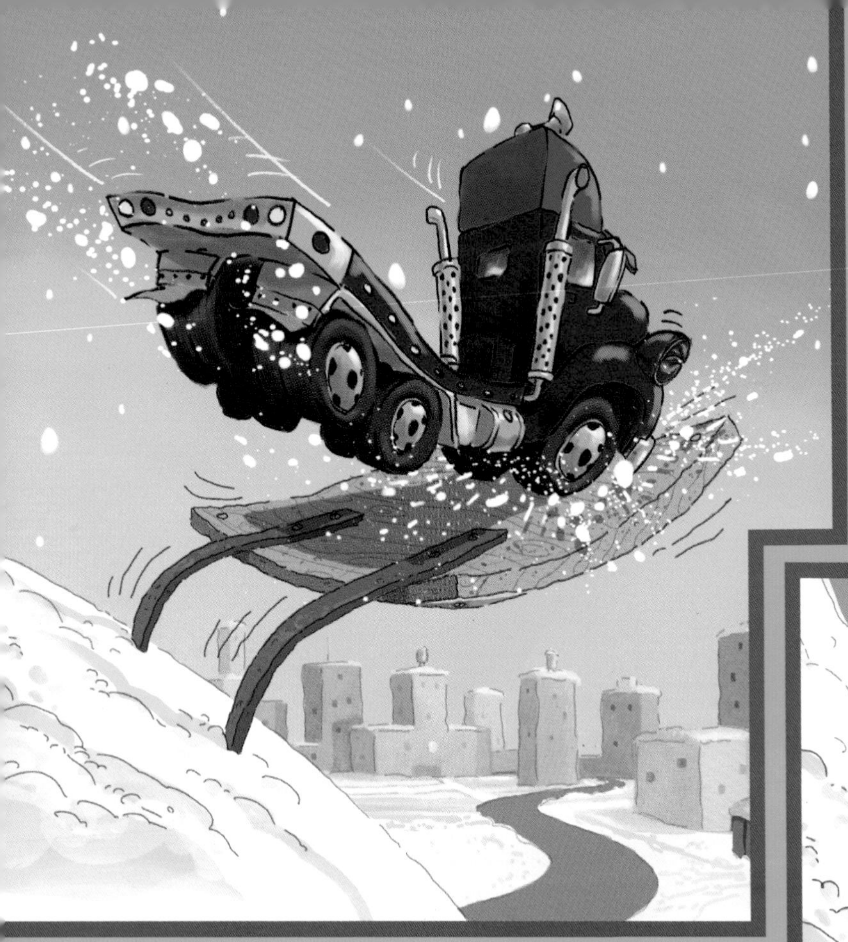

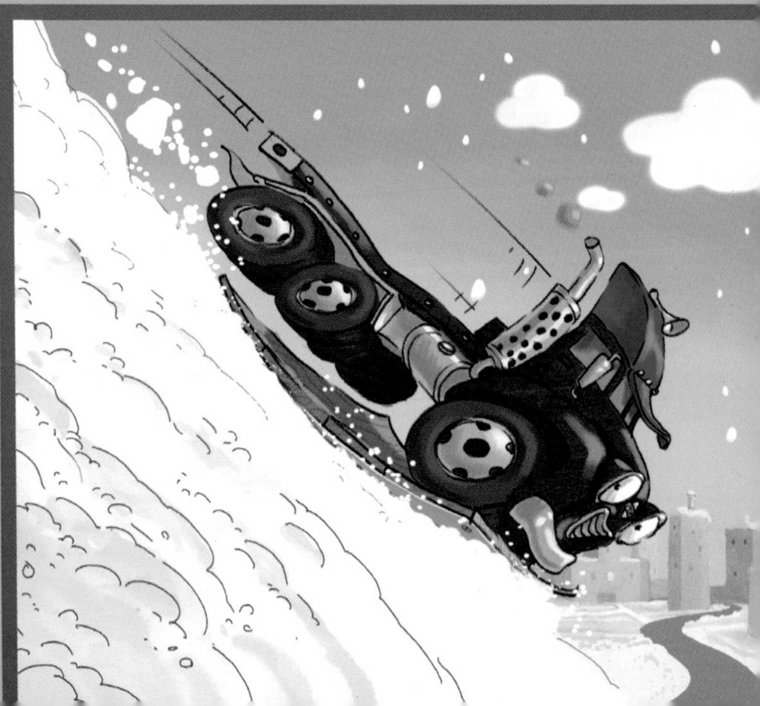

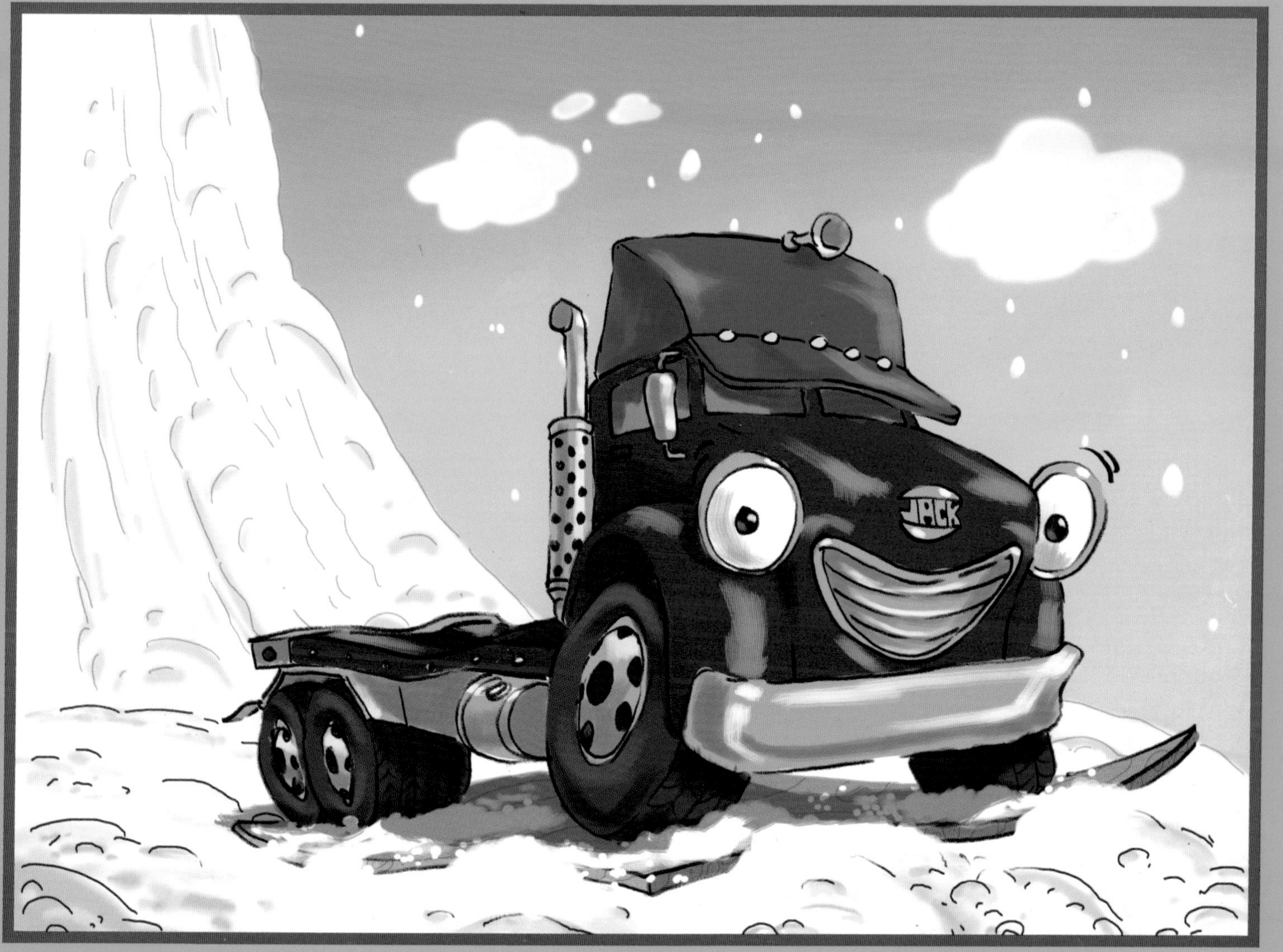
JACK

Help!

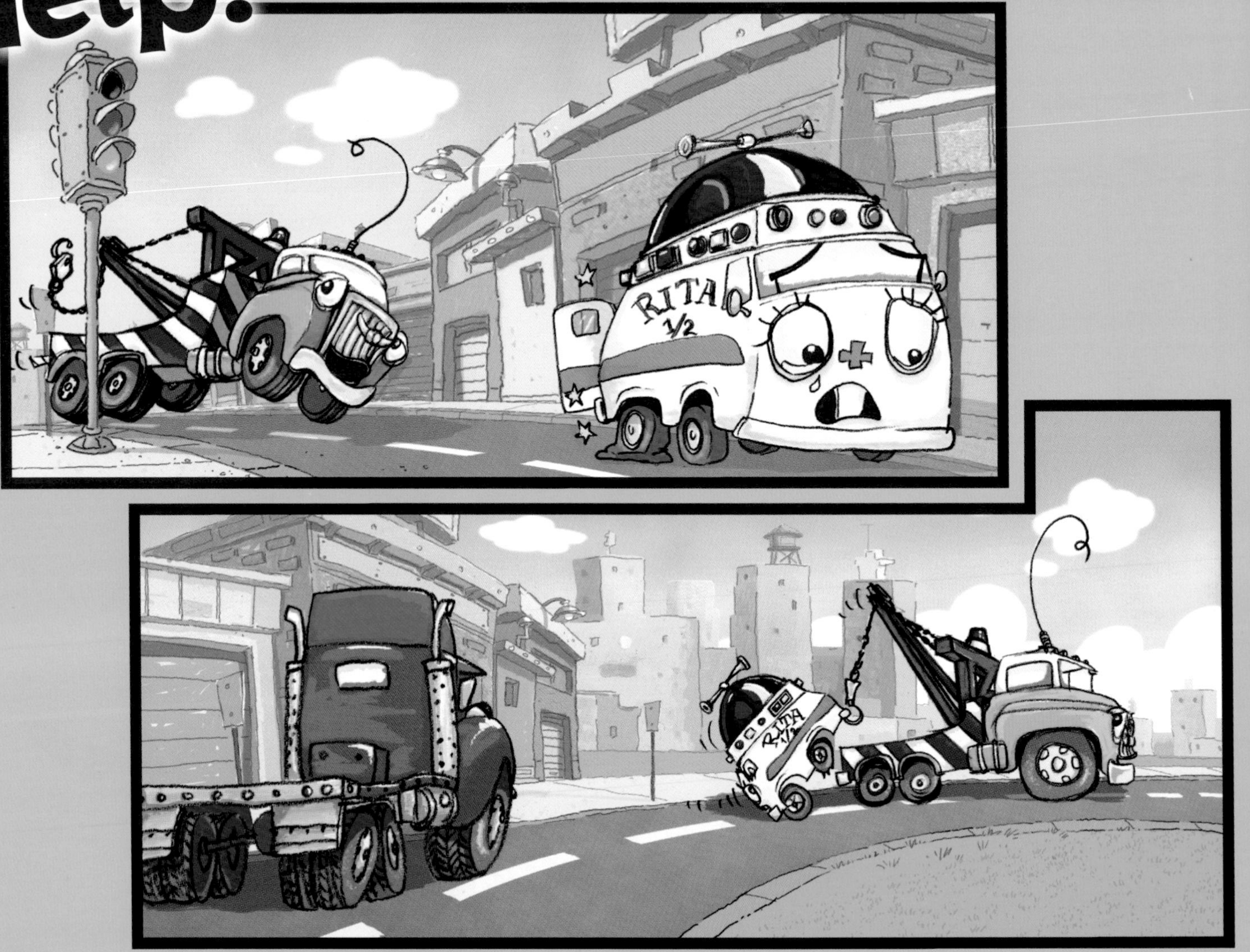

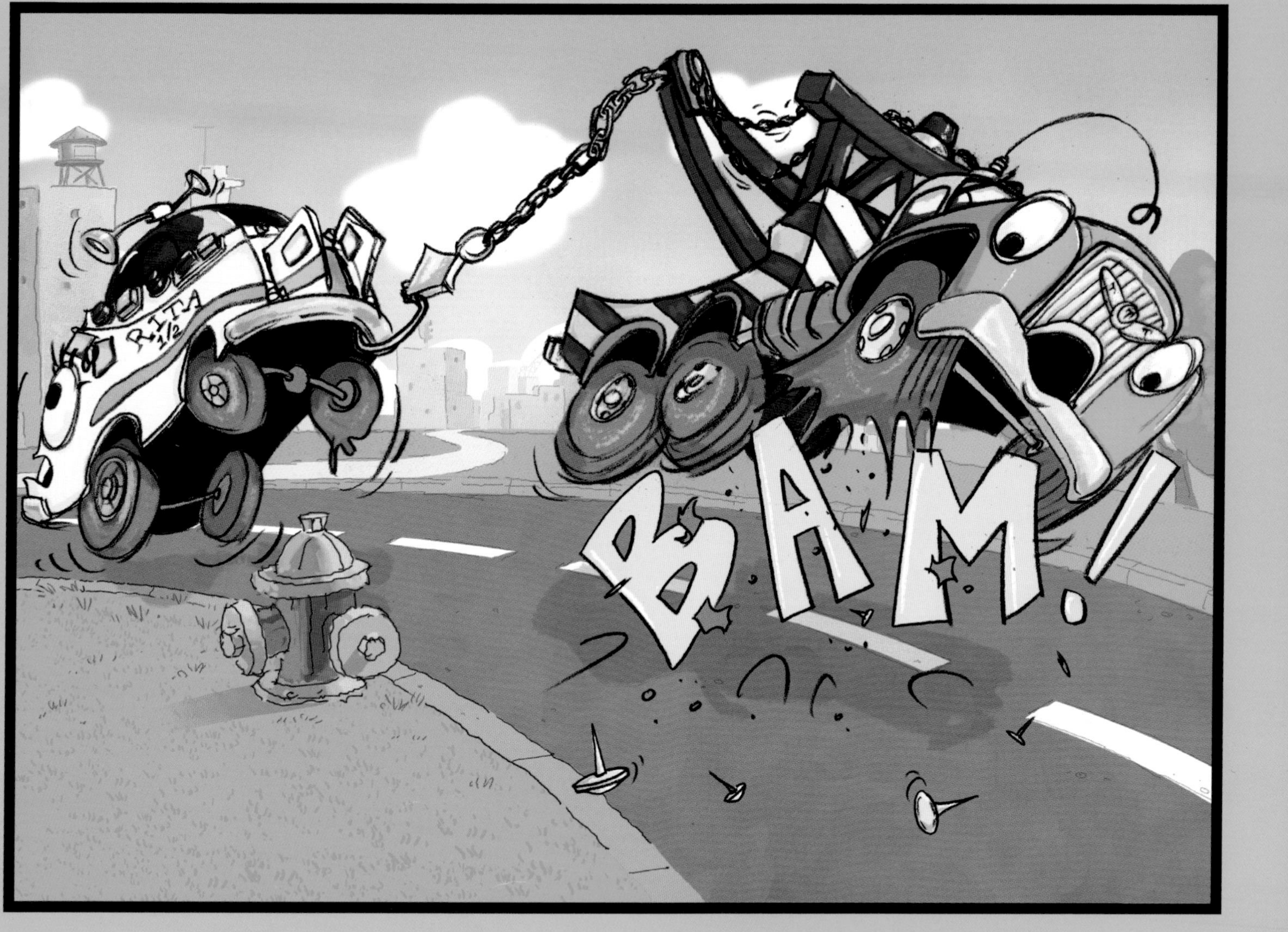
RITA 1/2
BAM!

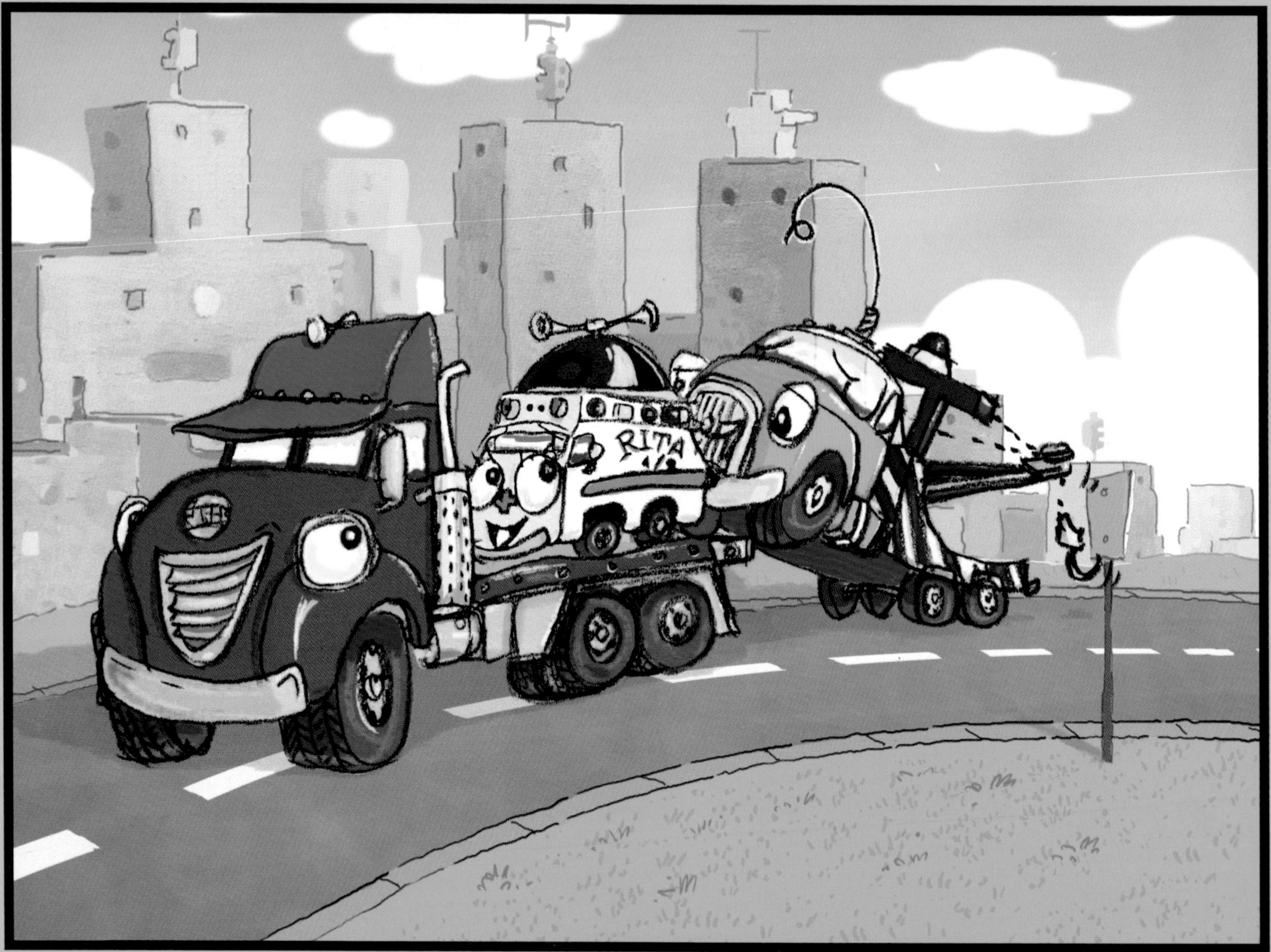
RITA